What's my number?

A person to play with, paper and pencils

Each write down a 4-digit number. Do

Take turns to ask questions to help gu   - only
answer 'yes' or 'no'.

Is your number bigger than 5000?

Is the thousands digit more than 7?

Is the hundreds digit less than 5?

6430

The first player to guess the other person's number wins. Play again.

> **In class** Play the game in two teams, Tigers and Lions.
> One child comes to the front of the class. The other team asks questions.

Add to the next ten

A person to play with, a dice, counters, paper and pencils

Look at each of these numbers.

| 34 | 28 | 72 | 63 | 46 | 87 | 39 | 54 |

Write how many must be added to get to the next
multiple of 10. Write what that multiple of 10 is.

Write three 2-digit numbers where 5 must be added
to get to the next multiple of 10.

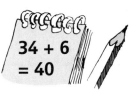

34 + 6
= 40

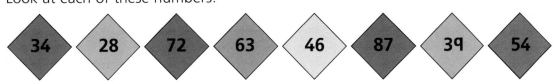

> **In class** Pair the children. They swap books to check their answers.
> If they disagree, they check with another pair.

1

Food prices

A person to talk to, a list of food prices or several supermarket receipts, paper and pencil

Look in the food cupboard. Choose a food. Write down its cost.
Discuss how much change you would get if you paid with one coin.
Write down five foods and their matching subtractions.

Bob's Supermarket
Butter... 70p
Bread... 56p
Beans... 46p
Soup... 39p
Total £2·11

50p – 46p = 4p

In class Discuss the different foods and the coins chosen.
Children could bring labels to create a display.

Along and across

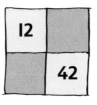

Paper and pencil

Use the first grid shown to help you.

23	77	100
66	34	100

89   111   200

12	
	42

46	
	35

62	
	58

Copy each grid and fill in the missing numbers. Each row should add up to 100.

Add the numbers in the columns.

Finally add the totals along the bottom, and then the totals down the side.

What do you notice?

Make up two grids of your own.

In class The children design their own grid for a friend.

Minute racer

A person to play with, a watch or timer, a dice, paper and pencils

Throw the dice. Throw again and add the two numbers. Keep throwing and adding while the other person times you for one minute.

Record your total. If it is a multiple of 10, add a bonus of 10 points.

Swap round so the other person has a turn, while you time them.

The winner is the first to 100.

$$5 + 6 = 11$$
$$11 + 3 = 14$$
$$14 + \ldots$$

In class Play the game in pairs. Try seeing who can get to 100 in the shortest time.

And fifty

Paper and pencil

Look at the number on each balloon.

Write the number 50 more and the number 50 less.

Finally, write all the numbers in order, smallest to largest. Which is the largest?

392   967   601   222   885

815   375   287   126   444

In class Write all the numbers in order on the board. Check the children agree.

Times along and across

 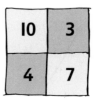

Paper and pencil

Look at the first grid.

2	5	10
8	3	24

16 15 240

6	10
4	4

8	5
4	5

10	3
4	7

Multiply the two numbers in each row and each column.

Now, either multiply the totals along the bottom or down the side (whichever is easier).

Write the final total in the corner. Repeat for each grid.

In class The children design their own grid for a friend.

A dicey game

A person to play with, a dice, paper and pencils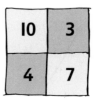

Take turns to throw the dice twice to make a 2-digit number.

Which 1-digit numbers divide exactly into your number?

Add any numbers you have found and find the total. This is your score for the round.

Play several times each.
The largest score wins.

$25 \div 1 = 25$
$25 \div 5 = 5$
1 and 5
$1 + 5 = 6$

In class Play the game in two teams, or class against teacher.

Move with the times

A person to play with, a dice, two counters, paper and pencils

4	3	2
5	6	10
3	4	6

Copy the grid. Each player places a counter on a shaded square.

The aim is to move from your start corner to the opposite corner. Take turns to move.

You may move in any direction (one square at a time).

You may not move to an occupied square.

As you move onto a new square, multiply the two numbers (old square number by new square number). That is your score.

When you have both reached the opposite corner, add up your scores. The lowest score wins.

In class Play the game in two teams, Oaks and Ashes. Pair up the children, one from each team. Add up the total score for each team at the end.

Double your age!

Paper and pencil

Baby
Grandpa
Teenager

Grandpa 60 → 120
Gran 55 → 110
Baby Jo 1 →
Mick 17

Write down the names of as many relations and/or family friends as you can. Write down their ages (guess if you don't know).

Double each person's age.

How old will they be when they are double their own age?

Write ten names and ages.

In class The children work in pairs to find half the age of each person.

Fours and eights

A person to play with, a dice, paper and pencils

Take turns to throw the dice twice to make a 2-digit number.

If you can make a number that divides exactly by 4, you score that number of fours.

32, I score 4 plus a bonus of 10.

If you can make a number that divides exactly by 8, you score that number of eights **plus** a bonus of 10.

$$32 \div 8 = 4$$
$$4 + 10 = 14$$

Keep playing, adding your score each time, until one person scores 50.

In class Play the game in pairs or teacher against the class.

How many slices?

Paper and pencil

Look at each fraction.

Draw the number of cakes and slices you would have with each fraction.

$1\frac{1}{4} \longrightarrow$

$3\frac{1}{2} \longrightarrow$

$2\frac{1}{5} \longrightarrow$

$1\frac{5}{6} \longrightarrow$

$2\frac{2}{3} \longrightarrow$

$1\frac{3}{4} \longrightarrow$

$4\frac{1}{3} \longrightarrow$

$2\frac{3}{8} \longrightarrow$

In class Children work in pairs to check their answers match. If not, they consult another pair.

Coin amounts

Coins, paper and pencil

Choose any coin.

(**2p**) (**1p**) (**20p**) (**50p**)

Imagine this is $\frac{1}{8}$ of the amount in a whole money-box. Decide how much money there is in the money-box and write it down.

Write $\frac{1}{2}$ and $\frac{1}{4}$ of that amount.

Choose another coin and repeat.

> **In class** Together, work out $\frac{2}{8}$ of some of the amounts. Point out that $\frac{2}{8}$ is the same as $\frac{1}{4}$. Repeat for $\frac{4}{8}$ and $\frac{1}{2}$.

Cross additions!

Addition/subtraction **N14**

Paper and pencil

Copy the number cross.

Choose one of the 3-digit numbers. Add 49 and write the total in the empty box next to it.

Repeat this for all four 3-digit numbers in the cross.

Make a cross of your own. Choose four 3-digit numbers and a 2-digit number ending in 9 to put in the middle.

Add the number in the middle to the other numbers and fill in the boxes.

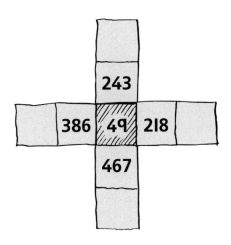

> **In class** Discuss what is special about the middle number.

Up to one thousand

A person to talk to, dice, paper and pencils

Take turns to throw the dice twice. Make each number a multiple of 100.

Add the two numbers.

The person closest to 1000 scores 100 points.

Continue playing until a player reaches 1000.

$$300 + 500 = 800$$

In class Play the game, teacher against children.

One hundred more or less

Place-value N16

Paper and pencil

Look at each of the star numbers. Write the number that is 100 more and the number 100 less than each number.

Write three numbers of your own. Write the numbers 100 more and 100 less.

1465   2679   4921   3004

8909   7110   6506   3910

In class The children work in pairs to check their answers match. If not, they ask another pair.

Adding the three

A person to play with, paper and pencils

Take turns to play.

Choose three of the ticket numbers. Add them in your head. Write the total and show your partner.

Your partner must decide which ticket numbers you chose and add them on paper. Was the guess correct? Had you added them correctly?

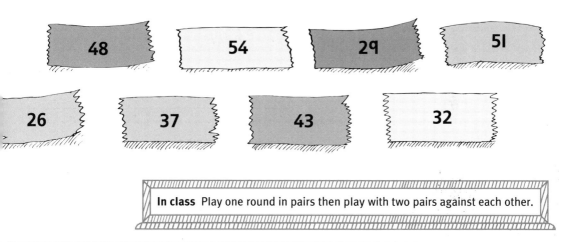

| 48 | 54 | 29 | 51 |

| 26 | 37 | 43 | 32 |

In class Play one round in pairs then play with two pairs against each other.

One thousand and one

Addition/subtraction N18

Paper and pencil

Write pairs of 3-digit numbers that add to make 1001.

One number should always be a multiple of 10.

Find at least ten pairs.

Try to choose pairs which are as different as possible.

$$350 + 651 = 1001$$

In class Discuss the different pairs and write some on the board.

Even differences

A person to play with, paper and pencils

One person decides to be 'odd', the other person is 'even'.

Each choose one of the kite numbers and write it down.

Work out the difference between the two numbers.

36

29

The difference is 7, odd ... you win.

odd *even*

29	36	44	53

62	74	81	95

If the difference is odd, the 'odd' person scores 5 points, if the difference is even, the 'even' person scores 5 points.

Choose two new numbers and play again.

In class Play the game, with one half of the class selecting 'even' and one half selecting 'odd'.

Different grids

Paper and pencil

Use the first grid shown to help you.

72	38	34
47	29	18
25	9	16

47	28
35	19

46	18
66	35

62	38
26	58

Copy each grid and find the difference between each pair of numbers. Write the difference between the row numbers down the right side of the grid and the difference between the column numbers along the bottom.

Find the difference between these new numbers. What do you notice?

Make up two grids of your own.

In class The children can design their own grid for a friend.

Threes and fours

A person to play with, a dice, paper and pencils

One player chooses to collect multiples of 3, the other to collect multiples of 4.

21, that's one of mine.

multiples of 3

Each write the first 20 multiples of your chosen number.

Take turns to throw the dice twice to make a 2-digit number.

If the number made is in your list you score 10 points.

The winner is the player with the most points after six turns.

In class Play the game in pairs, collecting multiples of 5 and 4.

×6 table

A dice, paper and pencil

Write out the ×6 table up to 12 × 6.

$1 \times 6 = 6$
$2 \times 6 = 12$
$3 \times 6 = 18$

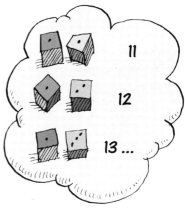

11

12

13 ...

Now write down all the 2-digit numbers you could make by throwing a dice twice. Which ones would be multiples of 6? Make a list of them.

In class Discuss which multiples of 6 you could make and which were impossible. What about 6?

Grid of nines

A person to play with, counters

Show someone in your home how to do the ×9 table on their fingers.

Copy the grid shown. Each place a counter on a shaded square.

The aim is to move from your start corner to the opposite corner. Take turns to move.

You may move one square at a time in any direction.

You may not move to an occupied square.

Each time you move onto a new square, multiply the number you left by 9 and score that number of points.

When you have both reached the opposite corner, add up the scores. The lowest score wins.

4	3	8
5	7	10
9	2	6

In class Play the game in two teams, Ants and Spiders. The children play in pairs, one from each team. At the end, add up the score for each team.

Multiplication square

Squared paper, a ruler, a pencil and a coloured pencil

Draw out a 10 × 10 multiplication square and write in the numbers.

3, 6, ...

Guess how many multiples of 3 there are on the grid. Colour all the multiples of 3. How close were you?

1	2	3	4	5	6	7	8	9	10
2	4	6	8	10	12	14	16	18	20
3	6	9	12	15	18	21	24	27	30
4	8	12	16	20	24	28	32	36	40
5	10	15	20	25	30	35	40	45	50
6	12	18	24	30	36	42	48	54	60
7	14	21	28	35	42	49	56	63	70
8	16	24	32	40	48	56	64	72	80
9	18	27	36	45	54	63	72	81	90
10	20	30	40	50	60	70	80	90	100

In class Discuss how many multiples of 3 there are on the grid. Did they remember to colour the multiples of 6 and 9?

One hundred times taller

A person to talk to, paper and pencil

Write down the names of six of your family or friends. Write their height in centimetres (or make a careful estimate).

Multiply each height by 100. How many centimetres tall are they now?

Write their height in metres as well.

In class Discuss how high a building is. After multiplying by 100 would the children's friends and relations be taller than a skyscraper?

Five foods

A person to talk to, paper and pencil

Choose four items of food or drink that you like. Write the price of each one.

Work out how much it would cost to buy five of each item. Write down the cost.

Now work out the total cost.

$5 \times 52p = 260p$

$\qquad = £2·60$

In class Discuss which items the children have chosen. Write some on the board.

Hidden vowel

A person to talk to, paper and pencil

Work out what the sentence says.

Use the vowel code below by finding the matching fraction.
For example, $\frac{3}{6} = \frac{1}{2} = a$.

Code $a = \frac{1}{2}$ $e = \frac{1}{4}$ $i = \frac{1}{5}$ $o = \frac{1}{3}$ $u = \frac{2}{3}$

Y $\frac{2}{6}$ $\frac{4}{6}$ $\frac{5}{10}$ r $\frac{2}{8}$ r $\frac{3}{12}$ $\frac{6}{12}$ lly $\frac{4}{8}$ m $\frac{2}{4}$ z $\frac{2}{10}$ ng.

In class Use the code to allow children to make up their own sentences.

Find a fraction

A person to play with, a dice, paper and pencils

Throw the dice twice to make a 2-digit number.

Can you find exactly $\frac{1}{2}$ or $\frac{1}{3}$ or $\frac{1}{4}$ of your number?

Choose a fraction you can use and work out that fraction of your number.
Score that number of points. Have 5 turns each. Write your total scores.

I've scored 7.

14

$\frac{1}{2}$ of 14 is 7

In class Discuss which numbers it is not possible to find an exact fraction of.

Car numbers

Paper and pencil 2

Draw five cars. Write five car number plates with a 3-digit multiple of 10.
Then write five numbers beside each car, all of which round to that car number.

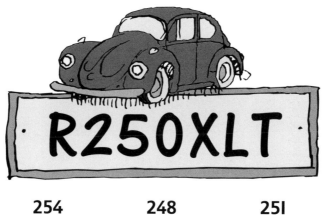

R250XLT

254   248   251
    249   245

In class In pairs, children share each other's car numbers.
Then they round each car number to the nearest hundred.

Code breakers

Addition/subtraction N30

A person to talk to, paper and pencil 2

Each letter is a digit. No digit is represented by more than one letter.
Work out what number each letter stands for.

m = 9 ...

**Hint: m = 9, h = 0
Two even numbers
are missing!**

```
    m  u  d
+   w  e  t
─────────────
 w  h  a  m
```

In class Discuss the solutions. What information did the children use to help them,
e.g. the fact that w must be 1? The children can work in pairs to create their own puzzles.

Darts

A person to play with, paper and pencils, a paperclip

Each player starts with 404 points. Make a 'dartboard' by drawing a circle split into six sections. Label the sections 1 to 6.

Take turns to spin the paperclip around a pencil to select a number. Use the number to make a multiple of 10 (for example, a 3 makes 30) and subtract that from the start number. Keep going like this BUT... if you spin a 1 you have to go back up to 404 and start again. The winner is the first to pass 0.

In class Play the game, children against teacher.

Different sides

Paper and pencil

Work out the differences between all the left-hand numbers and all the right-hand numbers.

Write down any pairs with a difference that is a multiple of 5.

86	144
49	153
36	121
27	141
78	102

In class The children work in pairs to write numbers on a table of their own. The differences must be a multiple of 5.

Wrong again

 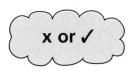

Look at all the subtractions below. Four are not correct. Work out which four they are and put them right.

x or ✓

4 1 0	4 8 2	3 2 8	5 4 1	6 2 8	8 1 1	9 7 2
− 2 6 5	− 2 5 6	− 1 6 5	− 2 3 6	− 4 2 4	− 6 4 4	− 3 2 8
1 4 5	2 1 6	1 5 3	3 0 5	2 1 4	1 6 7	6 3 4

In class The children work in pairs. Each child invents a subtraction and either writes a correct or an incorrect answer. They swap and check the subtractions.

Shaded odds

Look at the first addition grid. Each shaded square is an odd number. Each square that is not shaded is an even number.

Copy the empty grids and fill in any numbers so that each one has the correct type (odd or even). Find the totals for each row and column (they must be odd) and then add the totals. Your final number should be even.

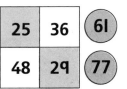
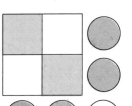
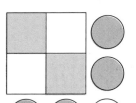
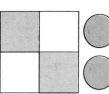

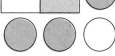

In class The children design their own grid for a friend.

Counting on down

 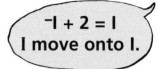

A person to play with, a dice, 2 counters, paper and pencils

Draw a number track like the one shown, from −10 to +10.

⁻1 + 2 = 1
I move onto 1.

⁻10	⁻9	⁻8	⁻7	⁻6	⁻5	⁻4	⁻3	⁻2	⁻1	0	1	2	3	4	5	6	7	8	9	10

Put both counters on 0.
Take turns to throw the dice.

If the number thrown is even, count on the matching number of steps.

3 − 5 = ⁻2
I move back to ⁻2.

If the number thrown is odd, count back the matching number of steps.

Write down the addition or subtraction for each move.

Remember odd numbers are subtracted, even numbers are added.

In class Play the game, teacher against the class.

Double or quit

Paper and pencil

Imagine you get £1 pocket money this week and then, each week after that the amount is doubled. How long would it be before you had £1000? Write down how you worked it out.

Week 1

Week 2

Week 3

In class Discuss how the children found their answers.

Fishy frenzy

A person to play with, paper and pencils

Take turns to choose a fish.

Read the number and multiply it by 3. Write down the multiplication and the total. After both of you have had five turns, add up each of your totals.

The winner is the player whose final total is closest to 1000. Play again.

In class Draw more fish on the board and let the children play in pairs.

Animal feeder

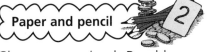

Paper and pencil

Choose an animal. Read how many pieces of meat it needs each day.

Look at the Meat Shop. Decide for how many days your animal can be fed completely, and how many meat pieces will be left at the end.

Repeat this for five animals.

49 pieces (shop)

6 pieces (wolf)

9 pieces (tiger)

10 pieces (lion)

4 pieces (bear)

5 pieces (panther)

8 pieces (leopard)

In class Discuss the different amounts left over each time.

Dicey division

A person to play with, 2 counters, a dice, paper and pencils

Each put a counter on 'Start'. Take turns to throw the dice and move the matching number of spaces.

Divide the number you land on by the dice throw number. Write down the division (including remainders).

Check the answer with your partner and score any remainder from the division.

If you throw a 1, you must move back one space.

Keep playing until both players reach 'Finish'. The highest score wins.

start

30 31 32 33 34 35 36 37 38 39 40 41 42 43 44 45 46 47 48 49 50 51 52 53 54 55 56 57 58 59 60

FINISH

In class The children invent their own division track game.

Along the line

Paper and pencil

Write the numbers in order of size from smallest to largest.
Write three more numbers to go at the end of the line.

3·9 5·4 1·7 2·2 0·9 1·4

4·5 0·1 3·6 0·5 1·2 1·5

> **In class** Present a similar problem using different numbers.
> See how quickly pairs of children can order them.

Value for money

A person to talk to, paper and pencils

Choose one of the pictures below. Each write down how much you think
the item would cost. Then compare your guesses. Whose guess was more?
Decide an amount both of you agree on. Draw the item and write down
the amount. Repeat for four more items.

> **In class** Discuss the different prices and agree which ones are realistic.

Taking away

Paper and pencil

Choose two frisbee numbers. Subtract the smaller number from the larger.
Write your subtraction. Repeat six times.

372   181   738   529   481   618   903

In class Discuss the pairs chosen. Work through some they didn't choose.

Race the clock

A person to play with, paper and pencils, a clock or watch

Set a timer or put a piece of Blu-tack on the clock
so that you can time five minutes.

Choose a list each. Set the timer and try to answer
all the questions in five minutes.

Check through the answers together.

I	£6·21 − £3·57	**I**	£7·35 − £4·68
2	I have £3·63. How much more will I need to save to have £5?	**2**	I have £3·58. How much more will I need to save to have £5?
3	What is four hundred less than 135?	**3**	What is four hundred less than 261?
4	Subtract 306 from 1000.	**4**	Subtract 404 from 1000.
5	Find the difference between 363 and 636.	**5**	Find the difference between 484 and 848.

In class The children can invent their own quiz.

How far?

Write down five places that you visit regularly. They can be fairly near or far away. Write down the distance from your house in metres or kilometres. You may have to convert the miles into kilometres.

Mary lives 500 m from me.

Gran lives 80 km away ...

Remember
3 miles = 5 km

In class Make a list of some of the chosen places. Which place was furthest away? Which place was nearest?

Heavy weight

What is the heaviest object in your home? It must be inside not outside. Draw it and write its approximate weight in kg (discuss it with someone else if you can).

Fold your paper in half. Write three clues on the back to help someone guess what the object is.

1. It has 4 legs.
2. It is full!

In class Children work in pairs to read each other's clues and guess the objects and the weights. Discuss the objects and the clues. Choose some objects as a whole class.

Best value

A person to talk to, several containers with liquid in, paper and pencil

Look along the bathroom shelf or in the store cupboard. Write down the contents of the bottles or containers and how much each holds. Then discuss how much each bottle might cost. Which is the cheapest? Which is the best value?

SHAMPOO
FREQUENT USE
225 ml

Olive Oil
500 ml

In class Compare similar products from the children's lists. Which shampoo/type of oil is cheapest?

Initial areas

Squared paper, pencil and coloured pencils

Draw your initials and those of someone else you know on the squared paper. Colour them in. Count the squares and write the area of each letter.

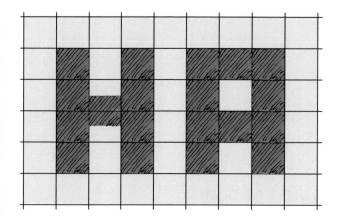

H = 9 square centimetres
A = 10 square centimetres

In class Write some signs for the classroom, e.g. Exit, Welcome, Paint Corner. Each pair takes a letter or word and works out its area.

TV screen

A person to talk to, a ruler or a tape measure, a television, paper and pencil

Find a TV. Measure the length of the long edge and the length of the short edge of the TV screen.

Add the two lengths and then double the total to find the perimeter of the TV screen. Write it down and draw the TV showing your favourite programme.

(If you don't have a ruler, use string to measure the perimeter and bring the whole length into school.)

> **In class** Make a display of the drawings and discuss the different ways they measured the perimeter. How many different-sized TVs are there?

Programme favourites

Time **M6**

A person to work with, a calculator, paper and pencils

Look in a TV guide and write the names of five programmes that you really enjoy. Write a.m. or p.m. to show when it is on.

Write the start and finish times of each programme and then work out how many minutes long it is.

Write the number of minutes beside each programme.

Robodog starts 4:15 pm
finishes 4:35 pm
20 minutes long

> **In class** Discuss how many minutes long each programme is, and which is the longest.

Months to look forward to

A person to work with, a calendar, paper and pencils

Look at the list of months.

January	
February	
March	
April	
May	
June	
July	
August	
September	
October	
November	
December	

MAY

M	Tu	W	Th	F	Sa	Su
1	2	3	4	5 Dentist	6	7
8	9	10	11	12	13	14 Lunch Sam & Sally
15	16	17	18 Gran's Birthday	19	20	21
22	23	24	25	26	27 Football	28
29	30	31				

Working together, decide which is your favourite month. Think of all the reasons why this is. Look at the day that the month starts and draw a calendar for the whole month. Think of all the special things that will happen in this month. Write or draw each one in the correct space on the month if you can.

In class Make a display of the children's month calendars. Chant the months in order.

Weekend joy

Paper and pencil

Copy the table shown and draw out a timetable for your weekend. Make it as funny as you can.

8:30	Stuck my head out from the duvet
8:40	Staggered to the bathroom
8:41	Finished in the bathroom
8:45	Burnt the toast

In class Discuss the children's timetables. Whose was most accurate? Whose was funniest?

Minutes of age

A person to work with, a calculator, paper and pencils

Think about an older person that you know. Work out how many minutes old they are. Think about the number of minutes in an hour, hours in a day, days in a month... Write down all your multiplications. Draw a picture of the person and write their age in minutes.

I'm 55 years old.

In class Make a display of the drawings. Discuss how many minutes old the children might be.

Shape drawings

Paper and pencil, coloured pencils

Draw four different regular polygons. Each one should have a different number of sides.

Write the name of each shape then try to make it into a picture. Give each picture a title.

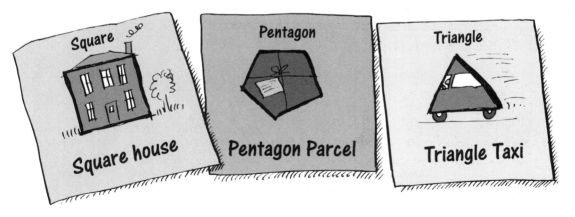

Square — Square house

Pentagon — Pentagon Parcel

Triangle — Triangle Taxi

In class Show the pictures without revealing the shape names. The class has to name the shapes.

Symmetrical guesses

A person to work with, scissors, paper and pencils

Fold a piece of paper in half. One person draws a triangle against the line. The other person cuts it out.

Score 10 points if the hole in the paper is triangular. Have two turns each.

Are any of the triangles equilateral or isosceles?

In class Discuss how the children made the two triangles.

Symmetrical shapes

Paper and pencil

Look at all the shapes below. Copy them and draw in any lines of symmetry.

Look around your house and draw some symmetrical shapes or objects. Bring all your drawings into school.

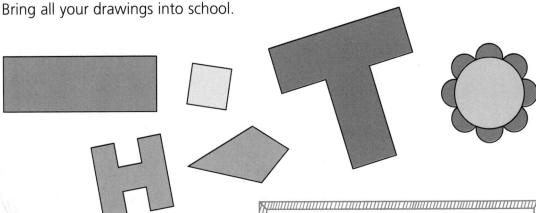

In class Discuss some of the examples they found.

Pyramids

A person to work with, a piece of card, scissors, glue/sticky tape, pencil and crayons

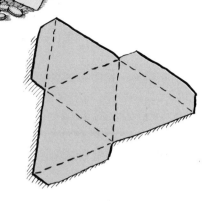

Copy the net shown here. Cut it out along the thick black lines. Fold it along the dotted lines. Decorate the sides and then stick it to make a tetrahedron.

In class Make a display of all the children's pyramids by hanging them on thread from a line.

Triangulation-point home

A person to talk to, paper and pencil

Copy the compass directions shown below. Think about places that are in each direction from your home.

'Triangulation-point markers' are found on the tops of hills or high points – they mark places you can see around you. Draw a triangulation-point marker with at least one place in each direction from your home.

Consult your family or friends to help you think of interesting places to put on it.

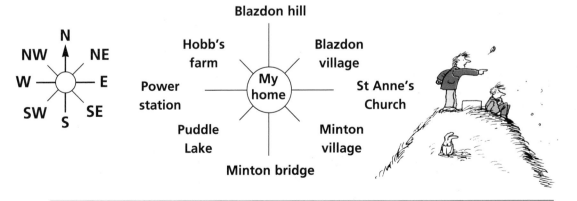

In class Discuss their choice of places. Have children chosen similar places? Display their work.

Right on

A person to talk to, paper and pencil

Look around your home. Find some examples of things that turn, such as door handles and clock hands. Draw your examples. Find at least one example of something that turns through 360 degrees.

Write the number of degrees the other examples turn through, if you can.

In class Discuss the different examples the children found. Which were common? Which were unusual?

Where's the shark?

Paper and pencil **2**

Study the grid. Write the coordinates of the following: shark, dolphin, boat, swimmer, rock and raft.

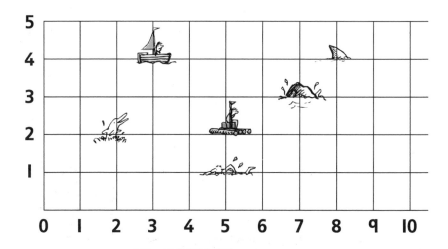

In class Draw a space scene on the board. Ask children to give you coordinates for stars, planets and rockets and draw them on the grid.

Crockery count-up

Paper and pencil

Copy the table below and make a tally chart of the crockery in your kitchen.

Crockery	Tally	Total
Small plates		
Mugs/cups		
Cereal bowls		
Large plates		
Large serving bowls		
Egg-cups		

In class Draw a large tally chart on the board. The children feed in their data. Discuss.

Hair raising

A person to work with, paper and pencils, crayons

Write a list of all your friends and relations. Write their hair colour.

Write the number of people with each hair colour on the pictograph shown.
Now draw your own. Draw one circle for every 4 people in each category.

Hair colour of people I know

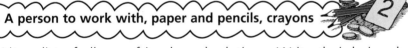

Hair colour

grey
blonde
red
brown
black

Key

 = 4 people

Number of people

In class Draw a large pictograph on the board. Fill in all their data. Discuss.

Computer count-up

Paper and pencil 2

Look at the graph
and answer the
questions.

How many children
have CD players?

How many have PCs?

How many have
videos?

How many have
radios?

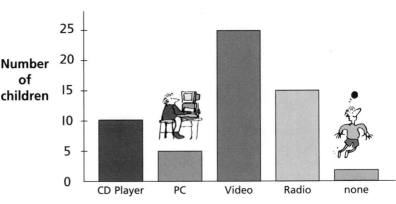

Types of electronic equipment children have at home

Number of children

25
20
15
10
5
0

CD Player PC Video Radio none

Types of electronic equipment

How many children have none of these?

Which type of electronic equipment does there appear to be most of?
Which does there appear to be least of? Why do you think this could be?

In class Discuss the graph. How much do the different items
cost? What relevance might this have to our data?

Venn diagram

Paper and pencil 2

Copy the Venn diagram.
Write as many numbers
on the diagram as you can.

Take care to check that
each number is placed
correctly on the diagram.

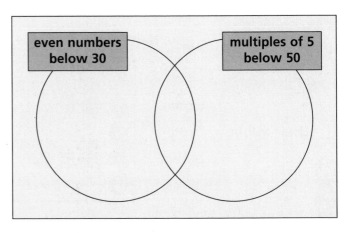

even numbers
below 30

multiples of 5
below 50

In class Discuss the diagrams. What happens if we add a third set, 'multiples of 6 below 60'?